The Harnham Water Meadows

history and description

Sarum Studies 3

Hadrian Cook
Michael Cowan
Tim Tatton-Brown

Contents

Front Cover photo, a prize winning study of Salisbury Cathedral by Tim Kidner of the Salisbury Camera Club

First published in the United Kingdom in 2008, on behalf of the Sarum Chronicle Editorial Team and Harnham Watermeadows Trust, by The Hobnob Press, PO Box 1838, East Knoyle, Salisbury SP3 6FA.
© The Harnham Watermeadows Trust 2008

British Library Cataloguing in Publication Data
A catalogue record for this book is available from the British Library.

ISBN 978-0-946418-73-2
Typeset in 11/13 pt Octavian. Typesetting and origination by John Chandler
Printed in Great Britain by Salisbury Printing Company Ltd, Salisbury

1
Introduction: What is a Watermeadow?

Town Path connects Long Bridge in Queen Elizabeth Gardens, at Mill Road in the city of Salisbury to the Old Mill Hotel at West Harnham. A casual visitor will most probably be aware that they are walking through the Harnham Water Meadows on a 'green finger' of countryside into the centre of the city. Manifest on what might be an otherwise flat floodplain are watercourses, hatches (sluices) and associated stone structures. Closer inspection reveals not only the regular pattern of channels, but also their association with ridges including channels cut in the top (correctly called 'bedworks', a set of which are watered from a single carrier), brick and concrete bridges, stone hatch structures with wooden paddles, and even a cast iron aqueduct. A glance at a map (Figure 6, page 20) will reveal they are located on a 40 ha [almost 100 acre] island caused by the split in the River Nadder located close to its confluence with the Salisbury Avon.

So what is a true 'watermeadow'? *It is an area of the valley floor grassland that is deliberately irrigated at the discretion of the farmer.* There is an infrastructure to achieve this but the objective is always to permit irrigation, or 'drowning' of grass, either to increase productivity or to bring production of grass forward in the spring; this is known as the 'early bite' to feed animals. Watermeadows have cultural significance in the minds of many because the Harnham Meadows, in front of Salisbury Cathedral, were immortalised by John Constable and other artists. To Thomas Hardy, watermeadows during drowning were described as 'meadows watered in a plan so rectangular that on a fair day they looked like silver gridirons' (*Return of the Native*, 1878).

Watermeadows need to be distinguished from other floodplain meadows on account of their sophistication. A meadow inundated because it is adjacent to a river is accurately termed a *flood meadow*; this is only wetted when the river naturally overtops its banks. Another designation, often confused with watermeadows, is a *grazing marsh*. This is similarly inundated by river (or sea near to the coast), is composed of alluvium, but has its water levels controlled through a network of ditches. Such areas include Romney Marsh (Kent), Walland Marsh and the Pevensey Levels (East Sussex), Halvergate Marshes (Norfolk) and parts of the Somerset Levels. The term 'marsh' accurately refers to areas of mineral soils (generally alluvium, of fine sand, silt or clay dominated topsoil). Peat areas, such as the Somerset Moors and Black Fens of East Anglia are strictly speaking termed 'fen' for calcareous peat or 'bog' for acid peat wetlands, including those in upland areas.

A true watermeadow is therefore a complicated and, of necessity, a labour intensive construction requiring absolute control of the water to function effectively. The process of creating water meadows is called 'floating', with individual irrigation events often referred to as 'drowning'. Water is caused to flow along the tops of specially constructed ridges, typically 3 to 10 metres (10 to 33 feet) wide, 0.5 to 1.0 metres (1.5 to 3 feet) high and anything from 10 to 200 metres (33 to 650 feet) long. It then trickles through the roots of the grass sward, eventually to drains that convey the water away, usually via a 'tail drain' to the river. The person who looks after the meadows and maintains the irrigation is usually called the 'drowner' in Wessex. Alternative titles include 'meadman', 'floater', or 'waterman' and there is confusion in some cases with the role of the water bailiff whose primary focus is the river.

Drowners supervise the watering of the meadows. This involves lifting a hatch to divert water into a 'main carriage' (a main stem irrigation canal that branches off a river) and thence along narrow trenches or furrows (termed 'carriers') typically up to 300 mm [one foot] deep and perhaps 300 mm wide. In order to control the flow of water, small pieces of turf or other material (termed 'stops') are inserted in the carrier or along its sides in order to maintain a flow of about 25 mm [one inch] deep through the grass. Water flows gently over the sides, and down the sloping panes to the drain. In doing so it soaks into the grass roots. Drowning is either of an entire meadow, or in sections controlled in this fashion – by opening and closing hatches and moving stops. A tail drain results from several drains running together and is the usual route by which water returned to the river.

The Harnham Water Meadows Trust currently owns or manages around 34 ha of the island and has been working to preserve, maintain or improve these historic watermeadows since 1990, following a long period of neglect.

2
The Origins of 'Floating'

T HE WORDS 'MEADOW' AND 'MEAD' are derivations of the Old English verb *mawan*, to mow – rather than graze. While watermeadows historically were valued for early grass, hay was frequently taken from them as well as from floodmeadows and marshes. A process know as 'warping', practiced variously on the Somerset levels and the 'warplands' of the Humber Levels, enabled grazing marshes or areas of floodplain to be irrigated by leading water across the surface so that nutrient bearing mud is deposited. The term 'wet meads', as used in earlier times, implies marshland. Such simple practices link floating with the earliest times; the ancient civilisations of Egypt, Mesopotamia and China all used nutrient bearing river water to fertilise agricultural land. Indeed, irrigation has been claimed as the basis of civilisation.

Floodplain alteration with the purpose of controlling water and widening options for agricultural or other economic activities is ancient in Britain as elsewhere. Many lowland alluvial and peat areas would have been un-drained during the Roman and Anglo-Saxon periods, although there are notable exceptions; land was reclaimed for agriculture in Roman times along the Severn Estuary and the Saxons settled and farmed on Romney Marsh, while the history of Fenland settlement and drainage is particularly complicated.

Meadow irrigation was certainly known in medieval France. The 'Description of Clairvaux', written in the twelfth century, by a monk of that Abbey in Burgundy, includes an account of how water was extracted from the River Aube in order to supply the monastic complex and its fish ponds, and to irrigate both vegetable plots and grass – a typically complex example of monastic water management. An artificial channel carried half of the extracted water to the monastery, where sluice gates controlled the flow to a grain mill. After this the same water was used for the preparation of beverages, and was then conducted to the workshops and kitchens. Finally, according to the account, it 'carries the waste products away' (presumably flushing the reredorter latrines) before returning to the river. The other channel was used to irrigate watermeadows (Box 1).

BOX 1. In the Description of Clairvaux, it is the other channel that is of particular interest:

Now that we have returned the stream to its bed, let us go back to those rills [or trenches] we left behind. They too are diverted from the river and meander placidly through the meadows, saturating the soil that it may germinate. And when, with the coming of the mild spring weather, the pregnant earth gives birth, they keep it watered too lest the springing grasses should wither for lack of moisture.

Irrigation also encouraged a bumper hay crop in the same account:

This meadow is refreshed by the floodwaters of the Aube, which runs though it, so that the grass, thanks to the moisture at its roots, can stand the summer heat. Its extent is great enough to tire the community for the space of twenty days when the sun has baked to hay its shorn grassy fleece. Nor is the haymaking left to the monks alone: alongside them a countless multitude of lay-brothers and voluntary and hired helpers gather the mown grass and comb the shorn ground with wide-toothed rakes.

The remains of probable medieval floating systems can be seen at English monastic sites, for example at Rievaulx in Yorkshire, and some form of irrigation system almost certainly operated at the great Benedictine abbey of Wilton, just 4km west of Harnham. Floating was perhaps already a technique familiar to some farmers in England. A seventeenth century writer refers to the practice of running 'water participating of a slimie and muddy substance' from 'land floods and fatte rivers' across meadow land in the spring. A clearer description, and one closely approximating to 'true' floating, was provided by Fitzherbert in 1524 (Box 2). By this time, sheep were the most profitable animals, and farmers were looking for ways to increase the number of sheep that could be fed over the winter period.

Watermeadow technology evolved from marshes, as 'meads' or, in the modern sense, floodmeadows. In general, areas of grazing marsh were too flat to provide a head of water sufficient for irrigation of grass. The advantage of introducing sediment containing nutrients (as in 'warping') is also appreciated early in the post-medieval periods. In the Wessex region, watermeadow systems are known at Affpuddle in the Piddle Valley in Dorset from the early 1600s supported by the manorial court. The early development of watermeadows owes much to energetic landlords and the Earls of Pembroke of Wilton House played a significant role in the adoption of the technology. Upstream from Harnham, in the Wylye and Nadder valleys, the earliest watermeadows were established at Dinton in 1625 on the Earl of Pembroke's land. In 1632, the Steward of the Manor of Wylye presided over the meeting of the Manorial Court when it was decided to establish and work water meadows. At Harnham, as elsewhere, we can furthermore find an intimate relationship with watermills because control of the river, including maintaining a head sufficient for irrigation, is common to both.

BOX 2. *The Book of Surveying and Improvements* by J. Fitzherbert in 1524, with the spelling modernised:

Another manner of mending of meadows is, if there be any running water or land flood that may be set or brought to run over the meadows, from the time that they be mown unto the beginning of May, and they will be much the better, and it shall kill, drown and drive away the moldye-warpes [i.e. moles], and fill up the low places with sands and make the ground even and good to mow. All manner of waters be good, so that they stand not still upon the ground; but especially that water that comes out of a town from every man's midden or dunghill is best, and will make the meadows most rankest. And from the beginning of May till the meadows be mown and the hay gotten in the waters would be let by and run an other way for diverse considerations...

3
The Sheep-Corn System

'From the latter part of the seventeenth century to the latter part of the nineteenth the floated water-meadow was one of the greatest achievements of English agriculture and an integral part of the sheep-and-corn husbandry of the downlands of Wiltshire, Dorset, Berkshire and Hampshire. In the Chalk of Wiltshire in this period the overwhelming majority of the several and common meadows by the streamside were floated.' (Eric Kerridge, 1953)

THIS QUOTATION relates to the abundance of floated meadows. Whether the meadows by a stream were held in separate (several) ownership, or whether commoners rights applied, the practice was the norm throughout the chalk downland valleys of the county.

Watermeadow technology is there to make the grass grow. The real impact of this technology has been to bring forward the 'early bite', although the hay crop later in the season was also of great value. Sheep pastured on meadowland (or 'brookland') had been folded on the arable at night since, at least, the Middle Ages and their dung and urine fertilised arable fields on the valley sides. The introduction of irrigated water-meadows meant that the 'early bite' in the valley added to the grazing available early in the year so that more sheep could be kept over the winter as the downs became bare. More sheep provided more fertilization leading to either a richer corn crop or an extended arable area. From the early seventeenth century the arable crop provided the greater part of the local agricultural wealth, something which continued for some two centuries.

Figure 1 shows diagrammatically the meadow management, including the sheep-corn system operating during the early part of the

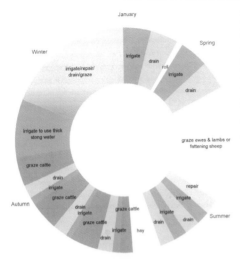

Figure 1 The all year round management of watermeadows after Boswell, 1779 (source: Stearne et al, 2002).

year. The practice of 'folding' sheep on arable to fertilise the often thin and partially eroded silty soils was probably ancient. Across southern England, downland agricultural systems in the late medieval period were differentiated into meadow or marsh grazing on floodplains, and arable on the valley sides, while historically much of the higher downland was sheep run. The classic model that developed in the Wessex chalklands (of Hampshire, Wiltshire and Dorset) was at its peak in the eighteenth and early nineteenth centuries. The Wiltshire Horn breed was said to produce little meat and no worthwhile wool; its value lay in its ability to transport and produce dung. While the sheep-corn system provided a diversity of products (meat, wool and corn), its ultimate survival depended on the farmer being able to command a good price for the grain.

However, to jump to a conclusion that watermeadows supported only one kind of agricultural system is to oversimplify. To illustrate, in the eighteenth and early nineteenth centuries, in the southern river Wey valley in Hampshire, Surrey and West Sussex (mostly a non-chalk river) water meadows seem to have been for haymaking to supply coaching inns of the Portsmouth Road. Today, in the Avon Valley north of Salisbury at Lower Woodford, cattle are grazed on the meadows as they are to the south east of the city, at Britford. Certainly haycrops from most watermeadows were greatly valued.

Until about 1600, sheep meat and fleece *were* profitable. However, by the seventeenth century, greater profitability could be achieved from wheat or barley grown on the slopes above the valley. Floating the watermeadows coincided with increased markets for corn, rather than for sheep products. It was an age of expectations on productivity – and hence – profitability, when arguably soil fertility was declining and there was not to be any 'artificial' fertilisers until the mid-nineteenth century. This meant that sheep manure and urine represented a valuable commodity fertilising the thin soils above the chalk, and these had experienced erosion since pre-history.

Drowning was controlled on a rota system with meadows divided into pitches, between stems that arose from branching channels, with dates indicating when a pitch was to be drowned for a few days. This was followed by what was called a 'dry period' that commenced with drainage. Dates were agreed (often in irrigation deeds) when irrigation could proceed. Drowning in winter or early spring varied by anything from a few days to a few weeks, but was typically between three and seven days.

Drowning commonly followed the 'Michaelmas Floods' (those around 29th September) such that an agreed and carefully planned rota commenced 1st November and continued usually until the end of April. Although records for the Harnham Water Meadows are sparse, Box 3 gives a clear idea from a nearby area about how this was achieved.

In mid-March, when the grass sward typically reached a height of 5 to 6 inches (120 to 150mm), ewes and lambs grazed the meadows between mid-morning and mid-afternoon. They would then be folded on the side slopes of valleys in the Downs overnight so that their dung and urine would fertilze the wheat and barley fields, and their hooves encourage tillering [root & shoot development] in the young cereal crop when already established. Towards the end of May the sheep were removed from the meadows and the grass left to produce a hay crop. From June to the end of September dairy cattle would often be grazed;

BOX 3: An extract from the Enclosure Award Commissioners Directions for watering in Odstock, Homington, West Harnham and Netherhampton in 1787:

The Principal hatches across the river in the first stem and also such hatches, trunks and other works as are or shall be made or erected in the main carriages within the first stem, shall be from time (be) made, erected and at all times repaired by the occupiers of the lands in the first stem. The occupiers of the lands in the second stem shall pay the occupiers of the first stem 10 pence in every 2 shillings for the expense of making, erecting and repairing hatches, trunks and other works as well as the expenses of the repairs thereof done in or about the month of November 1785 as those to be done in the future.

The owner and occupiers of the lands in each of the said stems shall have the sole use and management of all the said hatches, trunks and water carriages during the time that each of them are watering their lands in the said stems respectively.

The watering to begin the 1st day of November and be used for 8 days in the first stem and 6 days in the second stem and continue in that manner for 6 turns to each stem. And on the 24th day of January to begin to be used alternatively 6 days in the first stem and 4 days in the second stem for 4 turns to each stem which will end the 3rd or 4th day of March yearly – from which time the 4th of May the said Meadow is not to be worked.

Immediately after the 3rd day of May the said first stem is to be watered for 3 days and the said 2nd stem for 2 days and so alternatively for 4 turns which will end the 23rd Day of May yearly. Immediately after the Hay is carried off the said meadow the first stem will be watered for 3 days and the 2nd stem for 2 days alternatively for 2 more turns each.

and these proved destructive to the meadow surface and the banks of watercourses, needing remedial work in the autumn. Fresh topsoil and chalk were sourced locally and used to restore badly affected areas.

In this respect, the Harnham Water Meadows present an historical problem. There is no record, be it visual or written, for sheep on the Harnham island during the nineteenth century. Investment in the meadows during the 1850s by the Earls of Pembroke included prominent concrete sluices and cart bridges that point to hay production being important. Hay production, perhaps the major crop from the meadows, is likely because of the market to feed horses in the city. Negative evidence for an absence of sheep is not conclusive; there may be an absence of early season photographic or artistic record when it is possible that sheep were grazing. However, moving large flocks comprising up to 500 couples (of ewes and lambs) twice a day for several weeks through any of the three fords during spring high water levels would be impracticable. This situation pertained until 1869 with the construction of a bridge between Harnham Road and the south-eastern tip of the 'island', not to be confused with the medieval Ayleswade Bridge that crosses the entire river system at Harnham. Until this time, the track beside Town Path causeway could only be reached by fords at both ends, with a third ford on the site of the bridge to the south-eastern end of the island. There were, however, footbridges associated with the Town Path causeway since the eighteenth century. It is likely that the late investment of the 1850s related to growing hay crops that were easily transported for sale in Salisbury.

4
Location, Ownership and Occupancy

DESPITE THE PROXIMITY of the meadows to both the City of Salisbury and West Harnham, there are few direct historical references to the Harnham Water Meadows. Those watermeadows managed or owned today by the Harnham Water Meadows Trust are only a part of the watermeadows that existed within the parish of West Harnham. They are furthermore relatively unusual in being located on an alluvial island caused by a split in the River Nadder (watermeadow systems are typically beside rivers or within meander loops). The arrangement enables off-takes at several convenient points between the split in the Nadder and upstream of the impoundment created by the mills. This enables the passage of water over the surface, eventually returning to the river system via drains. For the western meadows, this included the tail drain that feeds the channel alongside Town Path.

At Harnham, water was diverted on to the meadows in a fashion that benefits from the impoundment of the river at the mills. Water flowed beneath the mills and re-joined the river that flowed around the mill complexes at Fisherton and Harnham (in this case, it still does). Behind the main sluices beside Harnham Mill is Rose Cottage, where the drowner most probably lived. A fuller description is given in Section 5; however there is a series of main carriages and carriers fed from the river (Figure 7, page 22, areas B&D). For example, behind the cottage, and running through the garden, is a large, stone, brick and concrete-lined main carriage controlled by a hatch, the Martin's Mead Hatch that flows over an aqueduct above a drain but below Town Path at point 8 in Figure 7. A significant volume of water can be diverted from the river to drown Martin's Mead (points E & F). A second very important main carriage

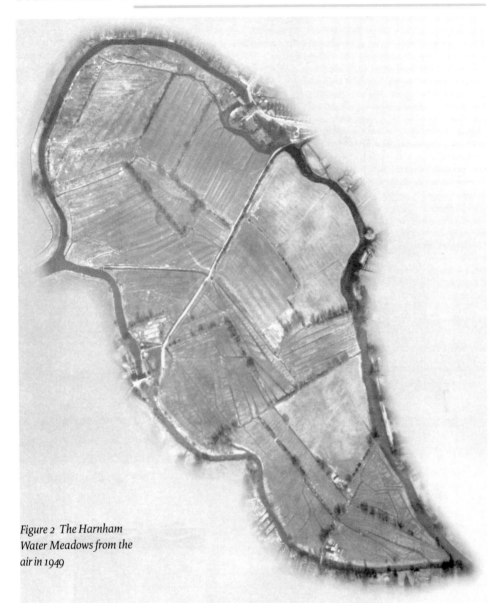

*Figure 2 The Harnham
Water Meadows from the
air in 1949*

was controlled by a triple hatch on the Great Mead (point 1), close to the
split in the Nadder (on the north-west side of the 'island') that feeds the
eastern meadows. Water came directly from both branches of the Nadder
but always above the impoundment at the two mills. The miller and water
bailiffs or drowner(s) would have had to agree to the timing and degree
of water control for both the mill pond and the carriers.

Neither are there direct accounts of the construction of the Harnham
Water Meadows, a disappointing finding when compared with other

systems. However, circumstantial evidence based on the regional context goes some way towards redressing this problem that arises (most probably) from a fragmented pattern of land holding and ownership where it would be easy for records to be lost. Figure 2 (modified 1949 air photograph) suggests that the 'floating' infrastructure fitted into both a pre-floated marshland landscape (on the natural 'island' formed by the split in the River Nadder with its own drainage system) and that allowance was made for fragmented land holding. There are vestiges of earlier strips in the watermeadows, some of them owned in the eighteenth century by Parsonage Farm (earlier this formed a part of the Salisbury Cathedral Prebend of Coombe and Harnham) that must be medieval.

In 1574 the former royal manor of Britford was sold to Thomas Gorges, the builder of Longford Castle, and in 1576 William Blacks Gent. became Lord of the Manor of West Harnham. The two manors within the parish of West Harnham were separated for the first time. From this date, land in West Harnham was leased to different people – for a fixed number of years, for life, or it was held in trust for another person. The Earls of Chatham are said to have held lands in Harnham between 1576 and 1689; but from 1687 to 1691 Sir William Pynsent Bart. of Urchfont and Odstock contracted, with different individuals, to buy the manor of West Harnham. Unfortunately there are no details naming the manorial steward, or exactly when drowning of the watermeadows was established. One of the agreements does, however, say that the owner of the premises paid 6/8d yearly in rent to control the flood hatches.

In his *Systema Agriculturae*, John Worlidge of Petersfield in 1669 could describe the watering of meadows as 'one of the most universal and advantageous improvements in England within these few years'.

Figure 3 William Stukeley's view of Salisbury in 1723

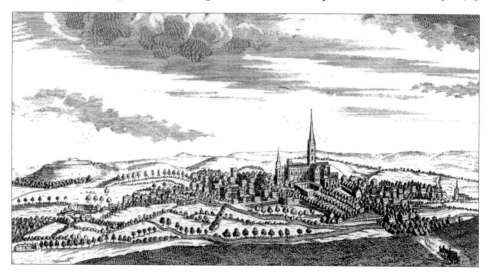

In the same year, an indenture (or contract) mentions:

'all that water meadow grounds lying next to the Dwelling House [Parsonage Farm at West Harnham] and all that water meadow lying nigh Fisherton Mills and also all the Water meadow commonly called Marsh meadow containing by estimation 3 Acres.'

From then on, water meadows near Fisherton Mills (see Figure 7, page 22) are often mentioned, but no details of when or by whom they had been established are given. Since the land was leased or rented to different tenants, individuals may have been responsible for making and working their own meadows. It was the custom of tenants, when they decided to float meadows, to have the agreement ordered, recorded and enforced by the Manorial Court – the Court Baron.

In 1691, there was also mention of a marsh meadow near to Fisherton Mill. Indeed, it is likely that there were similarities between the arrangements of watercourses that enabled mills to operate. Because the origins of floating lay in the juxtaposition of mill streams, races or 'leats' (taking water to mills at a high level) and mill tails (removing water at a lower level), there was also a weir enabling a diversion of excess water from the mill race. 'Mill hams' or Norman 'millehumes' were small meadows adjacent to a mill and were capable of being irrigated.

The manorial system controlled resources of land, water and labour, and policed its tenants. It was hence a powerful regulatory institution and Wessex was no exception. It was not until the Earl of Pembroke became Lord of the Manor of West Harnham in 1743 that we find a record of several tenants being presented at Court for 'not properly working the water meadows' for 'not cleaning a ditch' and for 'not repairing the bank of a carrier'. Not only are these recognisable – and essential-functions on watermeadows necessary to permit efficient operation, but we immediately recognise the need for communal water management, a situation that is worldwide in extent. From then on, the Earl of Pembroke's Steward was in charge of making sure the meadows were being properly maintained and operated. The parish of West Harnham was actually divided between Lords Pembroke (at Wilton House) and Radnor (who resided at Longford Castle). By this time, the Earl of Radnor had acquired the other manor in the Parish, known as West Harnham Walronds.

Figure 3 shows Stukeley's sketch of Salisbury in 1723. It is sufficiently detailed to indicate the layout of meadows at the southern end of the island which is recognisable today. As late as 1787, the detailed 'inclosure map' of West Harnham parish, includes, for the first time, the details of the meadows that lie within the parish (around one-third of the island lies within Britford Parish), their owners, and it also shows where all the main carriers were situated. The shape of the river channels is remarkably similar to the modern day, pointing to channel stability around the 'island' upon which the meadows are located. This reflects efforts to maintain the *status quo* because of the functioning mills and meadows around Fisherton and West Harnham, although the inherent nature of the channels with constructed and vegetated river banks impart stability.

The detail of the channels around Fisherton Mill in the eighteenth century is shown from Naish's Map (1751 ed). The small island immediately east of the Long Bridge is visible on the Inclosure map of 1787, but has since merged with the north bank of the river. (Figure 12, page 30).

Figure 4 shows the relevant extract of this Inclosure Map of 1787 and the overall pattern of main carriages remains today. The north and south branches of the River Nadder feed the mills at West Harnham and Fisherton Anger that were fitted with undershot wheels. The Old Mill Hotel and former Fisherton Mill are referred to in Sections 8 and 9. These are joined by Longbridge Lane (today this runs alongside the Town Path), and we may observe a complicated pattern of land ownership. The mills at Fisherton were demolished and the mill pond filled by 1970, only the mill house remaining from this large complex. Fisherton Mill is first documented in the Domesday Book (1086), and was an important mill throughout the Middle Ages.

In 1787, the principal landowners were the Earls of Pembroke and Radnor, but Thomas Walter Younge and 'Messrs. Whites and Coster' also owned some large meadows. Of particular note is the series of 'strips' or 'meads', as they are called to the south of the Fisherton Mills and Longbridge. There were two narrow strips (Woodward's and Quinton's), between Longbridge and Deanery Meads and two large strips (Rowlas and Parsonage Meads) south-east of the Town Path, that belonged to Parsonage Farm. These were probably part of the lands of the Cathedral prebend of Coombe Bissett and Harnham which had first been granted to the Dean and Chapter by Henry I in the early 12th century. It is likely that these are surviving strips in the meadows dating from the medieval period, before the meadows were floated. The earliest record of strips, or 'swaithes', at the southern end of the meadows is to be found in the 15th century Cartulary of St Nicholas' Hospital that still owns land at the southern end of the 'island', but this is in the parish of Britford. In 1787 the Harnham miller, Martin Neave, owned land adjacent to the mills (perhaps the original 'mill hamms' – that is, land adjacent to the mill that is watered at the discretion of the miller) as well as the small mead where Rose Cottage now stands. By the middle nineteenth century, the Gregory family owned the mills and associated land, they also bought other meadows. This estate remained in their ownership until 1899 and both mills remained in the same ownership until 1931.

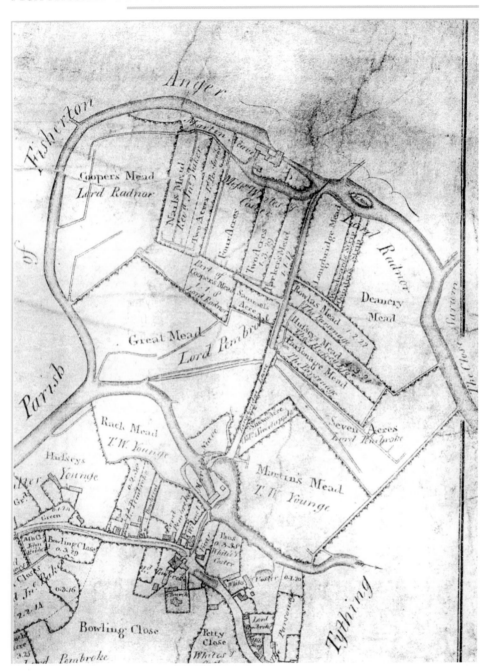

Figure 4 Extract from the Inclosure Map (1787) showing the Harnham Water Meadows.

During the mid-nineteenth century, largely after so much land elsewhere (both arable and commons) was enclosed, the Harnham Water Meadows experienced exchange of land between owners. At this time, the Earl of Pembroke invested considerably in improving the meadow infrastructure on his land, introducing the use of concrete, perhaps for the first time, on to a watermeadow system. New sluices, bridges and some channel revetments were constructed and irrigation rendered more efficient by new carriers from the south-west replacing the water supply to the meadows on the north side of the meadow which had come from the mill pond behind Fisherton Mill.

Both the efficient use of a mill wheel and watering meadows requires a head of water. Typically around one metre of head is required to successfully drown a set of typical bedworks, see Section 1) and, to achieve this, considerable engineering skill is employed. Seventeenth century construction involved dressed stone blocks housing wooden paddles that were raised or dropped to control the flow of water. Channel lining and 'hatch pool' (reservoir) construction also used dressed stone blocks of Hurdcott Stone, local upper Greensand quarried in the Nadder valley just to the west of Barford St Martin. By the early eighteenth century easier construction was achieved by using bricks. Early concrete (including shuttering) was widely used in the mid-nineteenth century, as in the twentieth, although breeze blocks are also evident.

By Victorian times hydraulic devices were well known and mid-nineteenth engineering works on the Harnham Water Meadows reflect this. An aqueduct (set in concrete) and invert siphons were introduced to carry the main carriages above or below drains respectively, thereby retaining an appropriate head of water (Figures 5a and 5b). An inverse siphon permits the recovery of the head of water on the opposite side of a traversed drain, despite the routing of the carriage *beneath* the latter. The most sophisticated of these (alas now gone) was the invert siphon from Springditch near to Churchfields Farm. The spring here was well above the level of the watermeadows and spring water was conveyed via

Figure 5 a (left) and b (above right) The Victorian aqueduct demonstrating its function to maintain a head of water above a drain, enabling the irrigation of Sammel's Acre

an inverse siphon in a tunnel under the northern branch of the Nadder to the extreme north-west corner of Cooper's Mead.

Figure 6 shows a sketch map of the meadows giving the names of the meads and selected other key features.

Sale documents show ownership of the Harnham Water Meadows during the twentieth century before the advent of the Harnham Water Meadows Trust in 1990. The Parsonage Farm estate (West Harnham) was sold in 1910 and included Nine Acres, Five Acres and Four Acres at the south eastern end of the island. A part of the medieval endowment for St Nicholas Hospital on Ayleswade Bridge was excluded. This is situated between Nine Acres and Four Acres alongside the River Avon (Figure 6).

In 1927, the meadows became part of Salisbury Borough and in 1931, Fisherton and Harnham Mills, Rose Cottage and various meads which were, until then, in a common ownership were broken up into various lots and sold. Lot 2 (Deanery Mead) was sold to the Dean and Chapter of Salisbury Cathedral for £1,200, while the Fisherton Mills were sold by Edward Francis Bowle to James Henry Bartlett for £3,900. The sale document of 1931 listed Longbridge, Deanery, and Hussey's Mead east of the Town Path, Ivy (or Cooper's) Mead, 'Part of Cooper's Mead', and the strip along the south bank of the (north branch) of the Nadder including Fisherton Mill itself in Figure 6, and today incorporating Fisherton Island. Rose Cottage and its garden (including 'Neave's Mead') were also included in the sale. West Harnham Farm was sold in 1943 and the estate included all of Seven Acres and Snow's Acre east of Town Path, and the five strips opposite the Fisherton Mill complex, the Great Mead and the diminutive Sammel's Acre to the west of Town Path. Today, Rose Cottage is owned by the Harnham Water Meadows Trust and the Dean and Chapter retain freehold of much of the area east of Town Path.

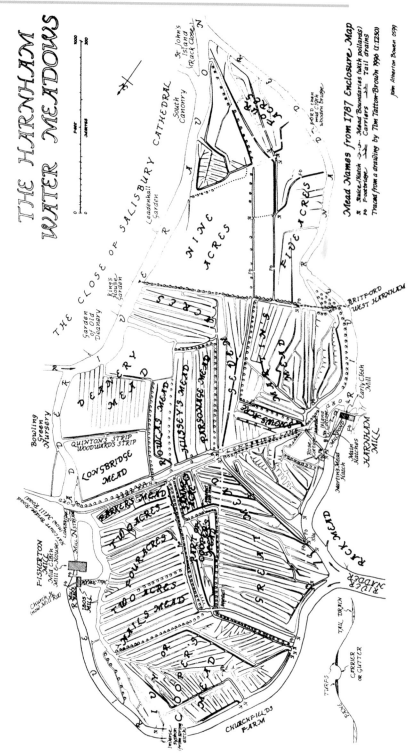

Figure 6 Sketch Map of the Harnham Meadows (after T. Tatton-Brown)

5
How did Drowning Work?

BEDWORK WATERMEADOWS are suited to valley bottoms where irrigation water is diverted from a river. In England these brought on the 'early bite' and enabled one or more hay crops to be grown later in the summer. The moving water proved efficient in carrying oxygen across the surface of the meadow, and into the soil to prevent stagnation in the root zone. Water allowed to stand for more than about two days will cause the oxygen contents in the saturated soil to fall to levels that are not suitable for grass to grow. By virtue of the water trickling gently through the panes of grass, the meadows found at Harnham are typical bedwork watermeadows, the zenith of a technology for grassland management that is designed to keep the water flowing and benefiting the grass from fertilisation from river water. They incorporate many features of floodmeadows, grazing marshes and warpland.

Designed to reach a compromise, bedwork watermeadows allow oxygen to be dissolved from the air in mobile water as it trickles through the grass. Some early watermeadows were 'floated up' by dropping a hatch at the exit point from the meadow, allowing water to back up behind; in these systems immobile water caused stagnation. On hillsides 'catchwork' systems (or catchmeadows) overcame stagnation by conveying water along the contour to overspill downhill, and thus irrigate the grass.

Oxygen is dissolved from the atmosphere during drowning and infiltrates into topsoil to prevent stagnation. With winter water temperatures in Wessex ranging typically between 6 and 9°C, the 70 to 90% of oxygen saturation (the maximum amount of oxygen that water can dissolve for a given temperature) in the irrigation water represents a

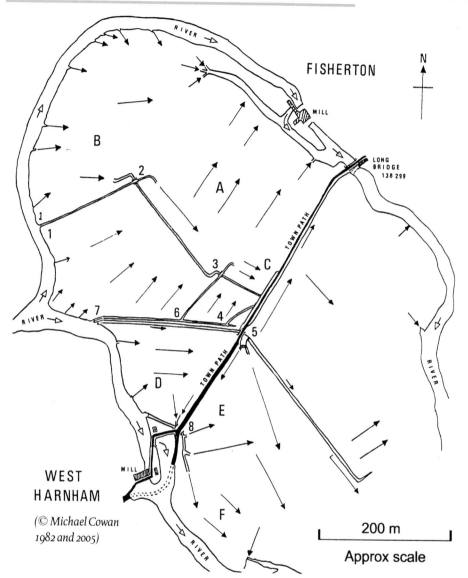

FISHERTON

N

MILL

B

LONG
BRIDGE
138 299

2

A

1

1

TOWN PATH

3

C

7

6

4

5

D

TOWN PATH

E

8

MILL

WEST
HARNHAM

*(© Michael Cowan
1982 and 2005)*

F

200 m

Approx scale

large flux of dissolved atmospheric oxygen over, and into, the soil. The other essential factors are temperature and nutrients. Water issuing from the chalk aquifer that feeds the rivers is typically between 10 and 12°c. By warming the soil above 5.5°c, during the winter and early spring, grass growth is triggered and the ground is protected from frost.

Nutrients such as nitrogen and phosphorus are brought on to the meadow from river water. Nutrients may be both dissolved in the water or else associated with silt, clay and organic particles that are mobile within the irrigation water, and they ensure good growth. Later in the season, irrigation can be practised to boost one or more hay crops. Then the water replenishes the soil water that was lost through summer transpiration; this is what is generally understood by the term 'irrigation'.

The Harnham Water Meadows Trust has succeeded, since 1990, in restoring winter irrigation to slightly less than 10% of the area. Figure 7 diagrammatically shows water coming on at the upstream side of the island and the system of main carriages, carriers and ridges, draining off to the south east where present water levels are 0.9 to 1.2m lower than those at the upstream end. Ground surface topographical elevations vary between about 1 and 1.8 m across the system from top (around the split in the River Nadder) to lower (south-east) end of the island.

Figure 7 (left) Irrigation of the Harnham Watermeadows.

There are a number of off-takes from the main river. Those on the north side feed area B, but main carriages of interest are located at points 1, 7 and upstream of point 8 where the off-take from the south branch of the Nadder crosses a drain on a brick aqueduct. From here, carriages branch off in five directions watering areas E and F. Main carriage flows are regulated by paddle hatches; that at point 1 feeds area A via a concrete invert siphon at point 2 that goes under a 'tail drain' to point 3. This is a concrete lined double bend, probably a meander inherited from the original drainage pattern of the pre-floated marsh. Over the tail drain is a mid-nineteenth century cast iron aqueduct that feeds Sammel's Acre. The tail drain joins the spillways from points 4 and 5, turning north-east and passing beneath the Town Path, eventually re-joining the north branch of the Nadder.

The configurations at points 2 and 3 probably reflect areas in different ownership requiring changes in watering arrangement in the mid-nineteenth century. From the iron aqueduct (point 3), area C ('Sammel's Acre') is watered; the flow once controlled at a single hatch at point 6. At point 7 is a triple hatch, set next to another single hatch that feeds water to Point 6. This large carriage takes water beneath the Town Path (at point 5) and, via a Hurdcott stone hexagonal junction 'hatch pool', onward to irrigate the eastern meadows, particularly 'Seven Acres' which returns water to the River Avon (downstream of the confluence with the north branch of the Nadder). South-east of here, while the meadows were once floated, the bedwork definition is poor and reflects long-term abandonment. Possibly the 'humose' (that is more peaty) soils found in this area were found unsuitable to sustain floating in the long-term.

6
The Fall and Rise of the Harnham Water Meadows

THE UNUSUAL NATURE of our 'island' meadows has been noted. The Harnham Water Meadows are, however, representative of extensive irrigation systems that once operated in the area. In any case, watermeadows are complicated systems and their survival depended upon their being able to achieve economic sustainability. The sheep-corn system was, above all, labour intensive and there was a competitive labour market throughout much of the nineteenth century as England industrialised. Wages needed to be found for the drowners, shepherds, water bailiffs, those who maintained the hedges, fences and pollarded trees and other agricultural labourers. Some commentators reported that watermeadows were in decline from the 1850s, the very time when the Earl of Pembroke was investing in the infrastructure at Harnham.

During the 19th century there were dramatic changes in farming methods, in Wiltshire as elsewhere. Mechanization was replacing manual skills, and as a result fewer farm labourers were required, which in some areas led to agricultural riots. The complex nature of work, involving water bailiffs, drowners and various skilled labourers was

gradually abandoned, especially because of the rising cost of labour. The use of artificial fertilisers meant that there was a simpler method of fertilising grassland and arable fields and widespread use of superphosphate fertiliser dated from the middle decades of the nineteenth century. Solving long-term problems of soil fertility obviated the need for folding animals on the arable fields at night.

The period of 'Victorian High Farming' ended in the 1870s, a blow to the domestic rural economy variously attributed to a spell of poor weather and the importation of grain and meat from abroad, including the introduction of refrigerated ships. This situation lasted until the outbreak of World War One in 1914, after which there was a labour shortage due to the slaughter in trench warfare and Spanish Flu. Another factor was the decline in sheep numbers between 1880 and 1950. Watermeadows were gradually abandoned, though some farmers continued to use them, especially along the Nadder, Avon and Wylye River valleys. Where watering meadows survived, this included a change from sheep to cattle. This process probably started in the middle nineteenth century with the introduction of railways and access to new markets, particularly for milk, although the demand for hay to feed horses continued into the early twentieth century.

Figure 8 a (below left) and b (above) Arthur Penton at work, clearing a carrier and opening a hatch (Nancy Steele)

Arthur Penton worked as a drowner on Lower Farm, Britford between 1963 and 1992, using traditional methods with amazing concentration and accuracy. The well-known pictures of him working are shown in Figure 8 a & b, with a ditching tool and opening a hatch.

Figure 9 shows examples of tools used by drowners. A selection of these can be seen at the Museum at Breamore House near Fordingbridge in Hampshire.

Figure 9 Examples of Drowner's tools

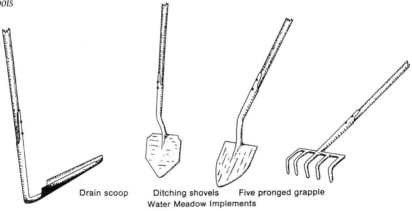

Drain scoop   Ditching shovels   Five pronged grapple
Water Meadow Implements

While the meadows around Britford continue in use today (feeding cattle) and the skills of the old drowners such as Arthur continue to the present generation of farmers in the area, detail of floating at Harnham is uncertain. The present condition, at least on the western portion, gives an impression of being operational – perhaps not very long ago.

The pattern of decline of the Harnham Water Meadows is unclear. Certain local people claim to remember proper 'drowning' in the 1940s and 1950s, even as late as the 1960s. Decline is likely to have commenced earlier in the century and one can speculate about the impact of the changes of ownership before and during the Second World War. Photographic evidence for the meadows, linked to infrastructural changes on the ground, suggest changes and abandonment including the loss of definition of bedworks on many of the Eastern meadows around this time. While it is plausible in wartime, there is no evidence for ploughing that also would have destroyed the definition of the ridges, carriers and drains. The main carriage flowing north-east from the hatch pool (reservoir) adjacent to and parallel with the Town Path that fed part of the Eastern Meadows was abandoned and the aperture blocked: Although exactly when is uncertain, the evidence suggests some time between 1937 and 1958. And the presence of a mature ash tree on the site of a carrier points to an earlier rather than a later date. Many control structures were robbed out for the stone in the 1980s and there may have been serious infrastructural damage of the predominantly humose or peaty soils in the period before 1990 when cattle and horses were grazed.

In 1986 the Dean and Chapter first negotiated to purchase a Z-shaped area of meadow east of the Town Path called Seven Acres so as to link together the two areas of meadows they had owned since 1931. Salvation arrived in 1989 with the formation of the Harnham Water Meadows Trust (HWMT) and in 1991, the formation of the Friends of the HWMT. The late Harold Cory, then the driving force behind the Trust, assisted in purchasing the western meadows 'to preserve the water meadows in their original state in perpetuity'. The formal charitable purpose of the HWMT is periodically revised, but the aim remains to maintain and improve the meadows in good condition and develop a public outreach programme. The Dean and Chapter retain freehold of much of the area east of Town Path but this is managed by the Trust on their behalf. The Trustees in 2008 are under the chairmanship of Lord Marland of Odstock and the Friends of HWMT (founded and chaired by Miss Jennifer Bowen) number around 400.

The Trust and the Friends have been able to develop a programme of involvement with the community, including the development of a Visitor and Education Centre at Rose Cottage. A systematic programme of major hatch restoration is near completion and there are regular discussions with the relevant agencies concerning activities as varied as restoring the river level for successful drowning and conservation management of a Site of Special Scientific Interest (SSSI) on the eastern meadows, opposite Salisbury Cathedral. An SSSI is an area of land which, in the opinion of Natural England (NE), is of special interest at a national level due to its flora, fauna or geological or physiographical features. NE provides notification of its significance and management to owners, occupiers, local planning authorities and the Secretary of State under the provision of Section 28 of the Wildlife and Countryside Act, 1981. Notification explains to owners and occupiers of a site's location and the features of special interest, how the land should be managed to maintain that interest and a list of operations likely to damage those features. The West Harnham SSSI is designated on the basis of its vegetation.

An academic conference at the Salisbury and South Wiltshire Museum brought together historians, archaeologists, ecologists, hydrologists and policy makers in March 2004, while a workshop in June 2006 looked forward to managing these historic watermeadows in a responsible way for future generations.

7
Rose Cottage

ROSE COTTAGE, WEST HARNHAM, is towards the end of the Town Path, on the northern bank of the south branch of the Nadder close to Island Cottage and the Old Mill. Dating from around 1840 (according to the Royal Commission for Ancient Monuments), this Grade II listed building probably housed the drowner, although the older Island Cottage, on the south bank opposite Harnham Mill on the Town Path, may also have fulfilled such a function. During the 1930s, Rose Cottage consisted of two downstairs rooms, an uneven staircase leading to a wide landing and a bedroom. Before the Second World War, one owner, Mrs Fox Pitt, had also purchased the meadow across the main carriage (that comes from the Nadder and through the garden to the Town Path and thence to Martin's Mead) to use as a garden. In 1787 this was recorded as belonging to Martin Neave, the owner of both Harnham and Fisherton mills.

The inter-war kitchen was apparently a lean-to affair, the water supply a standpipe and tap at the end of Island Cottage with the privy

Figure 10 Rose Cottage in 1931 from the Sale Document

Figure 11 Rose Cottage in 2006 following renovation

a galvanised iron hut. Rose Cottage, condemned in 1938, had housed the Evans family, said to have had many children and Mr Evans worked as a drowner. Between 1951 and 2004 the Cottage was lived in by a local teacher, Miss Jane Foster, who supplied information to the Friends of Harnham Water Meadows Trust in 2003. Her father purchased it from Mrs Fox Pitt. Mr Foster was an architect, and he managed to persuade the authorities not to condemn Rose Cottage so that the Foster family, comprising parents and three daughters, could enjoy the benefits of a 1950s renovation, most of which remained until 2005. The Cottage was purchased by the Harnham Water Meadows Trust in 2005 and was renovated over the winter 2005/6 to modern standards, but incorporating period features.

Today, Rose Cottage comprises a small tiled hall entered through french doors, a moderate sized living/meeting room, a practical modern kitchen, bathroom and WC. A short, uneven staircase leads to a small landing and thence two rooms, one a bedroom, the other used by the Trust as an office. The Cottage provides a central role as Education and Visitor Centre, enabling learning about meadows, and from where they can be enjoyed, while hosting meetings and community events related to the Trust's purpose.

Figure 10 shows the cottage from the Sale Document relating to the Fisherton Mills Estate in 1931 and Figure 11 shows the restored Cottage in 2006.

8
Fisherton Mill

THE MILLS AT FISHERTON AND HARNHAM were integrated into the watermeadows system and provided impoundment that raised the river level to enhance opportunities for irrigation of the meadows between both branches of the Nadder.

A mill is first mentioned at Fisherton (from the later Middle Ages, the Parish of Fisherton Anger) in the Domesday Survey (1086). However, Fisherton was a Saxon settlement, and it is possible there was a mill here considerably earlier. The impressive three-story mid-eighteenth century brick mill house and the arch by the front gate are all that remain of the corn-milling complex that once straddled the north branch of the Nadder. A single mill with a sluice gate to the west (on the site of the second mill) is first shown on a map of Salisbury by William Naish in c. 1716. Figure 12 shows a detail of the west side of this map, showing the church of St Clement and the mill at Fisherton, as well as the Town Path to the south east.

From the mid-18th Century, there was a range of mill buildings which formerly adjoined the house to the north-east, of three-stories with attics and brick walls with slate covered roofs. Probably later than the house, the mill itself was built of brick in at least two phases with three English-bonded western bays that were earlier than the two Flemish-bonded bays on the east. A similar range of mill buildings extended north-west from the mill house, parallel with the river. This was probably first built in the later eighteenth century, and then rebuilt between about 1800 and 1840 because it first appears on the Inclosure map of 1787. There was a third range, in the same alignment as this later range and it

Figure 12 Extract of Naish's map (1751 ed) showing detail of rivers. Fisherton Mill is bottom left below St Clement's Church.

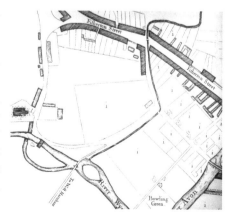

Figure 13 Fisherton Mill House in 1931, from the south

probably incorporated eighteenth century walls. It was probably this that was advertised in 1806 as the 'new-erected mill for machinery'.

In the later 18th Century, the mill pond supplied water via aqueducts over a tail drain to Ivy Mead, Nails Mead, Two Acres, Four Acres, Two Acres and Parker's Mead opposite the present day Fisherton Mill House. There was an exchange of meadows between Lords Radnor and Pembroke in the middle years of the nineteenth century and, in order to accommodate new ownership, new watering arrangements reversed watering in these meads and presumably improved drowning efficiency. Since then, these meadows have been irrigated from the north branch of the Nadder, close to the point of division of the river.

Figure 13 – the 1931 photograph of the Fisherton Mill complex shows an impressive development of a grist mill complex. Figure 14 shows John Constable's watercolour sketch of Fisherton Mill from Long Bridge in 1829. The mill complex extended across the present Mill Road;

Figure 14 Constable's sketch of Fisherton Mill From the Long Bridge in 1829. St Clement's Church lies to the right (British Museum).

however the industrial buildings were demolished to fill the mill pond in the late 1960s. Box 4 gives a chronology for Fisherton Mill.

BOX 4 *Chronology for Fisherton Mill*

1086: Mill worth 10s. at Fisherton in Domesday Book. New Sarum (Salisbury) did not exist at this time.

1273: Next mention of a mill, now worth only 30d. Owned by Maud, relict of Robert Walrand.

1303: A mill worth £4 belonging to Henry son of Aucher was attached to Fisherton Manor, this may be a second mill

1589: Two mills conveyed, with the manor, by Henry Ferrers to John Quarles.

1653: Three grist mills, with adjacent lands, conveyed (with manor, advowson etc) by Richard Lowe to Matthew Raymond.

1714: William Croome paying rates for the mill and by 1718 it is separated from the manor. Croome still in occupancy in 1736. For early references see V.C.H. Wiltshire VI (1962), p187.

Mid-18th century: New mill and second millhouse built, possibly by Martin Neave and shown on the 1787 Inclosure Map for West Harnham. He also owned the site of Rose Cottage.

1777: Owned by Mr Martin Neave, named as owner of both Fisherton and Harnham Mills on 1787 Inclosure Map for West Harnham.

Early nineteenth century: New enlarged mills are built.

1846: George Gregory succeeds Messrs Bell and Sutton as millers and H.G. Gregory are the mill-owners till 1899 (see Kelly's Directory)

1880: An extension is built on the south-west side of the millhouse.

1891 A two-sack roller plant was fitted (Wiltshire Archaeological Society Library at Devizes, sale catalogues XXIV. 20)

1899 Mills purchased by Messrs F. Bowle and Sons. He replaced the waterwheel with a turbine in the 1920s.

1931: On 10th October, the mill was conveyed from Edward Francis Bowle, Miller, to James Henry Bartlett for £3,900. He and his sons (from 1941) are recorded as being in occupancy 1953. Dean and Chapter purchase Deanery Mead (Lot 2) in the same 1931 sale, for £1,200.

1956: Occupied by Messrs H.R. and S. Sainsbury & co. Ltd.

1969: Whole site compulsory purchased, the mills demolished and the mill pond filled in. New 'Mill Road' created to join Crane Bridge to the Station. New cut made westwards from the tail from south-west of the mill to the main river, creating 'Fisherton Island', where 12 houses were built a few years afterwards.

1972: The mid eighteenth-century Mill House (listed Grade II*) bought by R. Tatton-Brown for £30,500.

9
Harnham Mill

HARNHAM MILL at the southern end of Town Path is built across a leat drawn from the River Nadder. Figure 16 shows the first known image, an 1803 watercolour by John Buckler (1770-1851) destined for Sir Richard Colt Hoare's collection at Stourhead. Buckler called it *Ancient Building at West Harnham* and was clearly not concerned to show that it was a water mill. This is the earliest known representation.

From a later (1834) illustration (Figure 15) it is possible to see virtually what is still there today, except that the first floor timber framing has gone. On the right, behind a high wooden fence is the cottage now known as Island Cottage, of undated origin and much changed but old enough to have been shown on the 1787 Inclosure Map (Figure 4, page 17). The wide pathway between it and the mill leads, out of sight, to a wooden bridge crossing the southern arm of the River Nadder above the weir and past the site where Rose Cottage would be built in the 1840s.

Figure 15 The Reverend Peter Hall's view of the mill in Picturesque memorials of Salisbury, a series of original etchings and vignettes ......etc 1834

It continued on a causeway across the meadows, now Town Path, alongside Longbridge Lane to Fisherton.

Salisbury was a large city (the seventh largest town in England by the late Middle Ages) and a new market for paper was emerging at the end of the fifteenth century. The long low stone and flint chequered building was built as a paper mill in the early Tudor period (i.e. c. 1490 to 1530). It was an expensively built structure that still retains its original roof, with the characteristic feature of double fireplaces at either end to dry the paper, with late Gothic windows and doorways. The taller adjacent nineteenth-century building was a yarn 'manufactory' built shortly after 1810. The two disparate structures are now in combined use as The Old Mill Hotel. The paper mill, one of the earliest in England, was built on the site of an earlier fulling, or cloth, mill known to have been in existence before 1299, occupied by the Pynnoks who were still in possession in 1374. Eventually, as Salisbury's medieval cloth industry declined, the fulling mill must have become redundant and a wealthy entrepreneurial individual invested in the newly developing market for making paper. As at Fisherton Mill, there may have been a mill here from Anglo-Saxon times.

Making paper involved pulping rags in troughs of water with stamping hammers raised and then dropped by tappets on the wheel shaft, as indicated in 1700 when the mill was sold, including the 'wheels, shaft, stockes, hammers, troughs and all other things belonging to the milling or beating of stuffe to make paper'. After two hundred years as a paper mill, by 1714 the building had reverted to fulling, using machinery not unlike that for making paper. By 1840 special machinery had been installed to grind bone meal. This machinery was taken out by 1879 when Mr Sangar leased the building as a tallow chandler and still occupied it in 1931, when the freehold was sold as part of the Fisherton Mill estate, for £405.

The adjacent four storey brick yarn factory was equipped around 1818 with 'a scribbling engine, two carding engines, nine jennies and two billies'. These were all big hand operated machines, so together with the mill a fair sized work force was involved.

In the last three-quarters of a century, the two buildings have probably seen more changes than in the whole of their preceding history. The factory was not part of the Fisherton Mill estate and hence not sold in 1931. Today they are linked and managed as one entity, the 'factory' as the bar and guest rooms of the Old Mill Hotel, the mill as its restaurant on the ground floor, domestic living accommodation upstairs. The factory has long been converted to its present role. The mill has been through many changes. At one stage it was a pottery, marked as such on the 1972

Ordnance Survey map, and there was a kiln where part of the hotel kitchen now stands. The millstone embedded in the outer kitchen wall is decorative, never part of the mill machinery in any of its manifestations over nine centuries.

Box 5 Gives a chronology for Harnham Mill.

BOX 5 *Chronology for Harnham Mill*

By the Twelfth Century a watermill, probably a corn mill, was established on this site.

1299: A documentary source refers to a 'fulling' mill where newly woven cloth was pounded by wooden hammers to compact the fibres, still used for fulling in 1374.

Around 1500, Early Tudor long low stone mill was built, almost certainly for paper manufacture.

By 1714 industrial paper making had ceased and the mill reverted to fulling.

Around 1810 the four storey brick building was built as a yarn factory equipped with carding machines to clean and tease the wool, and spinning jennies, to create the yarn.

1840s: The mill became a bone mill, grinding animal bones for fertilizer. Yarn factory was still in business

1879: The mill was let to a tallow chandler, making and selling cheap candles, who was still in business in 1931 when the building was sold

From the 1970s, the mill was later used in several ways, as a pottery and teashop, later combined with the former factory as The Old Mill Hotel.

Figure 16 Buckler's watercolour of Harnham Mill, (Wiltshire Archaeological and Natural History Society).

10
John Constable and Edwin Young in Salisbury

A RTISTS HAVE SOUGHT to represent the Harnham Water Meadows, although many people might be unconvinced that they wanted to depict the bedwork systems in any accurate or technical sense. Fortunately for posterity, plenty of eighteenth and nineteenth century accounts written for agricultural improvement achieved this.

During the summers of 1820 and 1829 the landscape painter John Constable (1776-1837) spent much time sketching and painting around the Harnham Water Meadows. In 1820 he was staying at the Bishop's Palace with the Bishop, Dr John Fisher, while in 1829 Constable was living at Leadenhall in the Close with his best friend Archdeacon John Fisher, the Bishop's nephew. A large number of sketches survive from this time at the Victoria and Albert Museum in London, and elsewhere, and they show the watermeadows in their heyday.

By far the most famous painting is his 'Salisbury Cathedral from the meadows' ('The Rainbow'), 1831 and which was first sketched in 1829. It shows a previously narrow wooden Long Bridge in the right foreground, with beyond it Longbridge Mead and Deanery Mead. After several oil-sketches, the magnificent final version was first exhibited at the Royal Academy in 1831, and is now in the National Gallery.

Edwin Young (1831-1913) was a Victorian artist, known to few outside his city of Salisbury. His life was something of an enigma. His father, a cobbler, died when Edwin was very young. His mother was left to raise eight children. He first worked as a surveyor for a local land agent. Later he was involved in the development of Milford, Salisbury.

View west across the watermeadows from Leadenhall garden to West Harnham mill and church. The poplar tree and 'Great Alder' are on the left hand side near the river. This oil sketch was made by John Constable in 1829 (Victoria & Albert Museum)

Pencil sketch by John Constable, made on 23 July 1820, looking north from Harnham Hill to the Close and Harnham watermeadows. Old Sarum is in the background. On the extreme left of the trees of the Close are the 'Great Alder' and poplar tree in Leadenhall garden (Victoria & Albert Museum)

Haymakers at Longbridge Lane (now the Town Path) by Edwin Young (detail)

Pencil sketch by John Constable from the Bishop's Garden, looking north to the cloister and Cathedral, c. 1820. (British Museum)

Two views of the Cathedral from the ford near Harnham Mill by Edwin Young, made in the late nineteenth century

Two views of hatches and carriers in the late nineteenth century by Edwin Young

A view of the double hatch near the main river, by Edwin Young (detail)

View SSW from the top floor of Fisherton Mill House of the carriers along the tops of the ridges in 1993

His artistic training is unknown, but in his early twenties he was known to be copying popular paintings of the day. He left nearly 400 of his watercolours and sketches of Salisbury and South Wiltshire to the city. Included in the bequest was the money to build a public art gallery and local art collection; the gallery was completed in Chipper Lane just before the First World War and the collection is now housed in the present Salisbury Library, along with the Edwin Young Gallery.

Further Reading

G. Atwood, 'A study of the Wiltshire water meadows', *Wiltshire Archaeological and Natural History Magazine* 58, 1963, 403-13

J.H. Bettey, *Wessex from* AD *1000*, Longmans, London, 1986

J.H. Bettey (ed) () *Wiltshire farming in the seventeenth century*, Wiltshire Record Society 57, 2005

G. Boswell, *A Treatise on watering meadows*, London, 1779

G.G.S. Bowie, 'Watermeadows in Wessex – a re-evaluation for the period 1840-1850', *Agricultural History Review* 35, 1987, 151-158

N. Bowles, *The southern Wey: a guide*, River Wey Trust, Liphook, 1988

H.F. Cook, 'Evolution of a floodplain landscape: a case study of the Harnham Water Meadows at Salisbury, England', *Landscapes* 2008 (1), 50-73

H.F. Cook, *et al*, 'Productivity and soil nutrient relations of bedwork watermeadows in southern England', *Agriculture, Ecosystems and Environment* 102 (1), 2004, 61-79

H.F. Cook, *et al*, 'The origins of water meadows in England', *Agricultural History Review* 51 (2), 2003, 155-162

H.F. Cook and T. Williamson (eds), *Water management in the English Landscape: field, marsh and meadow*, Edinburgh University Press, 1999 (see chapters by R. Cutting and I. Cummings, S. Wade Martins and T. Williamson and J. Bettey)

H.F. Cook and T. Williamson (eds), *Watermeadows: history, ecology and conservation*, Windgather Press, 2006

M. Cowan, *Floated water meadows in the Salisbury area*, South Wiltshire Industrial Archaeology Society (monograph series), 1982

M. Cowan, *Wiltshire water meadows*, Hobnob Press, Salisbury, 2005

M. Cowan, *Harnham Mill*, Hobnob Press, Salisbury (Sarum Studies 2), 2008

E. Crittall (ed), *A history of Wiltshire*, 6, 1962, 187 (Victoria History of the Counties of England)

R. Cutting, *et al*, 'Hydraulic conditions, oxygenation, temperature and sediment relationships of bedwork watermeadows', *Hydrological Processes* 17, 2003,

1823-1843

T. Davis, *General view of the agriculture of Wiltshire*, London, 1794

T. Davis, *General view of the agriculture of Wiltshire, with frontispiece map*, London, 1811

M. Everard (ed), *Water meadows: living treasures in the English landscape*, Forrest Press, 2005

E. Kerridge, 'The floating of the Wiltshire watermeadows', *Wiltshire Archaeological and Natural History Magazine* 55, 1953, 105-18

E. Kerridge, *The agricultural revolution*, Allen and Unwin, London, 1967, 251-67

P. Matarasso, *The Cistercian world: monastic writings of the twelfth century*, Penguin Classics, London, 1993, 285 to 292

W. Naish, *The City of Salisbury with the adjacent Close, church and river accurately surveyed* (printed map), 1716; 2nd ed 1751

O. Rackham, *The history of the countryside*, Orion, London, 2000

Royal Commission on Historical Monuments (England), *Ancient and historical monuments in Salisbury, 1: city of Salisbury*, 1980, 159 (500)

K. Stearne, *et al*, 'Water meadows in southern England', *Landwards* 57 (5), 2002, 2-6

Glossary of Terms

THERE IS A SOMETIMES CONFUSING TERMINOLOGY used when describing the infrastructure and operation of watermeadows. This would have developed casually with local or regional variations that can be ambiguous. One such term is 'drawn' (commonly, but not always, used to describe a top gutter along the top of a ridge) and omitted here. Terms here generally follow Davis (father and son) in 1794 and 1811, as used by Cowan 1982 and 2005, or have become commonplace in reference to the Harnham Water Meadows. Furthermore, certain terms from environmental sciences can appear obscure to the non-specialist.

Water falling as rain can either run-off as surface flow, or infiltrate into the soil to replenish rock formations known as **aquifers** (literally 'water-bearers') to occupy fissures in the rock. In Wessex the most important aquifer by far is the **chalk**, an unusually pure limestone of Cretaceous age, formed between about 100 and 65 million years ago. The importance of the chalk in supplying an even flow of water to rivers cannot be underestimated. Watermeadows are constructed on alluvial soils, generally deposited over gravels dating from the Pleistocene ('Ice Age') that are adjacent to the rivers. **Alluvium** is the deposit laid down by a river over time and, in this area, the soil it forms is calcareous (calcium bearing) and of slightly alkaline pH, making these especially suitable for the grass sward of the watermeadows.

The process of constructing an irrigated meadow is termed **floating**, hence *floated water meadows*. To operate the system (when watering or irrigating) is to engage in **drowning**, hence a **'drowner'** is the person in charge of the meadow infrastructure who controls irrigation.

Drowning involves taking water from upstream and returning it to the river downstream by means of **control structures** (correctly referred to as **hatches**, alternatively 'sluices') and a hierarchy of **channels**.

Hatches consist of a framework (generally stone, brick or concrete) into which slot one or more paddles (once constructed from elm, generally unseasoned oak today) which, when raised or lowered, control flow. It is important on watermeadows that water scours the bottom of channels to mobilize the sediment.

A **main hatch** upstream controls water into a a **main carriage.** This delivers water to either one or more **carriers**. In certain legal agreements the term '**stem**' is used. Water may also be delivered directly to carriers along the tops of **ridges** (often also referred to as **bedworks**), the sloping sides of which are **panes**. Small hatches, typically those used to drain carriages to drains once drowning is deemed to be sufficient, are called '**bunny hatches**' in Wiltshire. A carrier, when full, spills water, along its length, down the sides of the **panes** into the intervening **drains**.

Depending on the slope and discharge of water, **stops** are placed every few metres within the channel to slow the flow, or are placed at the side of the channel where overtopping flow to the panes needs to be reduced. Stops may be permanent or temporary, and are generally made of turf. However, logs or other available materials are used. Leaving a turf stop in a channel to constrain flow means it may become a permanent feature of the channel that reduces its depth at a given point. Stops within the channels along the tops of the ridges are commonplace at Harnham and may be visible, or are felt underfoot.

Other features include **invert siphons** that carry the main carriages above or below drains respectively, thereby retaining an appropriate head of water. An inverse siphon (a device not unlike the U-bend on a modern WC) permits the passage of water *beneath* a carrier or river, yet the head recovers on the other side such that irrigation of the tops of bedworks remains possible. **Aqueducts,** made of stone, brick or in the nineteenth century cast iron, are by contrast open channels that pass above another watercourse thereby also retaining the head of water.

A number of drains are consolidated into a **tail drain** (a main drain) feeding back to a lower point on the river. The channel beside the Town Path constitutes a tail drain for the western meadows for the Harnham system.

Acknowledgements

THIS SECOND EDITION (2008) is based upon an earlier publication by Nancy Steele and Tim Tatton-Brown. Jennifer Bowen (who is thanked for her editorial comments) supplied the 1999 photographs of the cast iron aqueduct. The Friends of Harnham Water Meadows Trust Committee gave their support in producing this revised history. The chronologies for Fisherton Mills and the Harnham Mill were compiled by Tim Tatton-Brown and Michael Cowan (who also supplied Figure 7) respectively. The photo on the front cover is by Tim Kidner, the Edwin Young pictures are by permission of The Edwin Young Trust and Annette

Ratuszniak. John Constable's sketch of Fisherton Mill from the Long Bridge and the pencil sketch from the Bishop's Garden are reproduced by kind permission of the British Museum. The Enclosure map of 1787 is from the Wiltshire and Swindon Archive Office in the Wilshire and Swindon History Centre. The aerial photograph of the meadows is from the Ministry of Defence. Buckler's watercolour of Harnham Mill is reproduced by permission of the Wiltshire Archaeological and Natural History Society. Nancy Steele provided the photographs of Arthur Penton. The sketch of Drowner's tools is by Elisabeth Church. The Victoria and Albert Museum gave permission for figures b & c, the National Gallery for Figure e.

Index

Numbers in **bold** refer to illustrations